SOCIAL SKILLS COMICS

HANDLING ANXIETY IN SCHOOL

AGES 7-12

By Michael Canavan
with Lawrence E. Shapiro, PhD

A Brand of The Guidance Group
www.guidance-group.com

Social Skills Comics – Handling Anxiety in School
© 2012 Childswork/Childsplay
A Brand of The Guidance Group
1-800-962-1141
www.guidance-group.com

All rights reserved.

ISBN: 978-1-58815-164-3

This book contains original reproducible activity handouts, exclusive with Childswork/Childsplay and is fully protected by copyright. The original purchaser of this book is authorized to reproduce and use the individual items in this book for the generation of creative activity in a psychiatric/therapeutic/educational setting. However, the reproducible activity handout collection in this book may not be reprinted or resyndicated in whole or in part as a reproducible handout book or collection, or for any other purpose without the written permission of the publisher.

This publication is meant to be used by an ADULT facilitator only. The handouts/activities should be photocopied for distribution, or if this book contains a CD, they can also be printed.

Printed in the United States of America.

TABLE OF CONTENTS

INTRODUCTION

Dear Reader,

Welcome! This book has been written to help you learn how to act in all kinds of situations that can come up at school.

In each situation you will:

- Meet the people in the situation.
- See a wrong way to handle the situation.
- See the way you are expected to behave.
- Learn what might happen when you behave the right way and the wrong way.
- Answer some questions about situations you may have been in.

You probably won't ever be in exactly these situations, but the skills you learn with this book may help you when you are in situations like these.

We hope you will learn something valuable, laugh a little, and have some fun, too!

1. BEING UNPREPARED FOR CLASS

Uh oh! Your basketball game ended late, and you didn't have time to finish your homework last night. Don't worry. Most people are unprepared sometimes.

Expected Behavior:

When you are unprepared for class, you should talk to your teacher about how to make it up.

Meet Juan:

Juan didn't read what he was supposed to last night.

Juan

Meet Ms. Russo:

Ms. Russo is talking about last night's homework.

Ms. Russo

THE WRONG WAY

Juan is not writing down any answers. Ms. Russo thinks Juan has done the reading. She is concerned when she notices that he is not working.

THE RIGHT WAY

Juan tells Ms. Russo he did not have time to do the homework. Ms. Russo tells him that he can make it up tonight.

Look at Juan in *The Wrong Way* comic. Can you see that he is upset? He does not understand the lesson.

Look at Juan in *The Right Way* comic. Can you see that he feels better? He is relieved that Ms. Russo knows he did not have time to finish his homework.

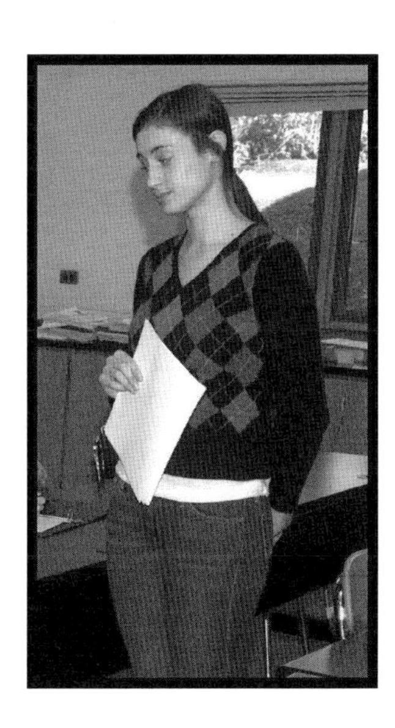

Look at Ms. Russo in *The Wrong Way* comic. Can you see that she looks concerned? By not speaking up, Juan has fallen behind.

Look at Ms. Russo in *The Right Way* comic. Can you see that she looks relieved? She is happy to help Juan get caught up.

What else could Juan have done to make up for not having read the homework?

Have you ever tried to hide the fact that you were unprepared for something? What happened?

Write about another situation where it would be better to speak up if you are unprepared.

2. READING IN FRONT OF THE CLASS

Reading in front of the class can make you nervous. What if you trip over your words or get distracted and forget what you are up to? Focusing on your task will help you do a better job.

Expected Behavior:

When you read in front of your class, you should concentrate on the task instead of the audience.

Meet Rich:

Rich has to read his report to the class. He does not like reading in front of the class.

Rich

Meet Ms. Larson:

Ms. Larson is listening to Rich read his report.

Ms. Larson

THE WRONG WAY

Rich is nervous. He is thinking about everyone watching him. He loses his place and repeats himself. His classmates and Ms. Larson cannot understand him.

THE RIGHT WAY

Rich reads his report in a clear voice. He keeps his mind on his reading and doesn't allow the audience to distract him. Ms. Larson thinks he did a great job.

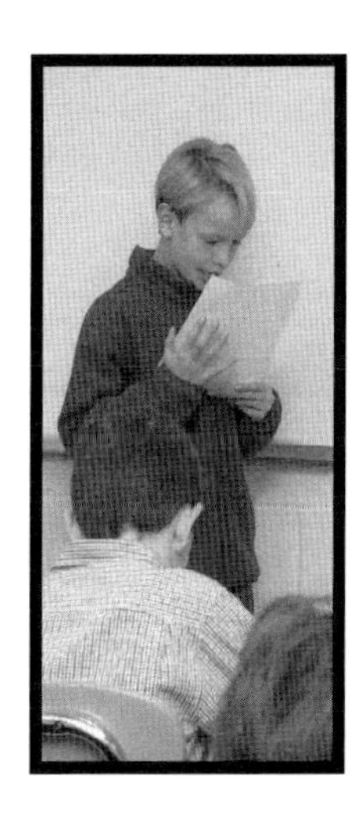

Look at Rich in *The Wrong Way* comic. Can you see that he looks uneasy? He is worried about everyone watching him.

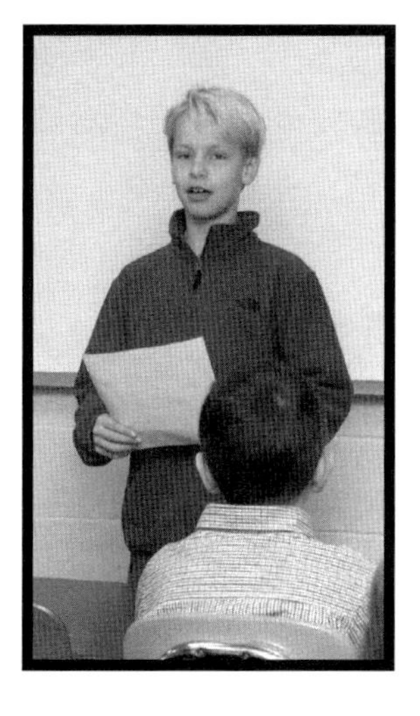

Look at Rich in *The Right Way* comic. Can you see that he feels comfortable? He knows his classmates are listening, but he is concentrating on his reading.

Look at Ms. Larson in *The Wrong Way* comic. Can you see that she looks concerned? She cannot follow what Rich is saying.

Look at Ms. Larson in *The Right Way* comic. Can you see that she looks happy? She likes the way Rich is presenting his report.

What else could Rich have done to stay focused on reading his report?

____

____

____

____

____

Have you ever had to read in front of your class? How did it make you feel?

____

____

____

____

____

Can you think of another time when you have to focus on a task in front of a group of people? Tell about it.

____

____

____

____

____

3. ENTERING CLASS LATE

Do you ever get to class late? Stopping at the office or getting something from your locker can make you late. It can be embarrassing to enter the classroom when you are not on time.

Expected Behavior:

When you arrive late for class, you should tell your teacher why you were late.

Meet Kate:

Kate is arriving for class late.

Meet Ms. Larson:

Ms. Larson wants to know why Kate was late.

THE WRONG WAY

Kate walks to her seat without saying anything to Ms. Larson. She mumbles when Ms. Larson asks why she is late. Ms. Larson thinks Kate is being rude.

THE RIGHT WAY

Kate first tells Ms. Larson why she is late. Then she sits down. Ms. Larson is pleased that Kate explained why she was late.

Look at Kate in *The Wrong Way* comic. Can you see that she is avoiding Ms. Larson? She is looking away while Ms. Larson is talking to her.

Look at Kate in *The Right Way* comic. Can you see that she is talking to Ms. Larson? She is showing Ms. Larson respect.

Look at Ms. Larson in *The Wrong Way* comic. Can you see that she looks annoyed? She is bothered by having to ask Kate why she is late.

Look at Ms. Larson in *The Right Way* comic. Can you see that she is ready to continue the lesson? She is happy that Kate explained her lateness.

What else could Kate have said when she entered the class late?

When you enter the room late, how does that affect your class?

Have you ever had to enter a class late? Did it make you anxious? What did you do?

4. DEALING WITH A BULLY

No one likes being bullied, but many kids are bullied sometimes. If it happens to you, it is important that you know how to deal with it.

Expected Behavior:

It is a good idea to ignore a bully who is giving you a hard time.

Meet Benjamin:

Benjamin is being bullied by Gabrielle.

Meet Gabrielle:

Gabrielle blocks Benjamin's way in the hallway.

THE WRONG WAY

Gabrielle stands in Benjamin's way and laughs. Benjamin hangs his head. He shows that Gabrielle is bothering him.

THE RIGHT WAY

Benjamin ignores Gabrielle and walks around her when she tries to block his way. He doesn't show any reaction to Gabrielle's bullying.

Look at Benjamin in *The Wrong Way* comic. Can you see that he is staring at the floor? He is letting the bullying make him sad.

Look at Benjamin in *The Right Way* comic. Can you see that he is walking away? He is not responding to Gabrielle.

Look at Gabrielle in *The Wrong Way* comic. Can you see that she is laughing? She is happy that she made Benjamin feel bad.

Look at Gabrielle in *The Right Way* comic. Can you see that she has stepped aside? She is frustrated. Benjamin will not respond to her.

What else could Benjamin have done to keep from being upset by Gabrielle?

Why do you think Gabrielle wants Benjamin to react to her?

Has someone ever bullied you? How did you react?

5. MAKING FRIENDS

It's great to have friends, but making new friends isn't always easy. When you are in a place where you don't know anyone, it helps to know how to make new friends.

Expected Behavior:

If you want to make new friends, you should smile and introduce yourself.

Meet Antonia:

Antonia is at a park she has never been to before.

Meet Kate:

Kate is playing on the jungle gym.

THE WRONG WAY

Antonia sits close to where Kate is playing. She waits to see if Kate will notice her. Kate doesn't realize that Antonia wants to play.

THE RIGHT WAY

Antonia walks up to Kate, smiling. She waves and introduces herself. Kate is glad that Antonia has joined her.

Look at Antonia in *The Wrong Way* comic. Can you see that she is just sitting there? She is not showing Kate that she wants to join her.

Look at Antonia in *The Right Way* comic. Can you see that she is waving to Kate? She is showing Kate that she wants to be friends.

Look at Kate in *The Wrong Way* comic. Can you see that she is playing by herself? She has not noticed Antonia.

Look at Kate in *The Right Way* comic. Can you see that she is smiling at Antonia? She is happy that Antonia will join her.

What else could Antonia have said to let Kate know she wants to be friends?

What could some of the other kids on the playground have done to be friendly to Antonia?

Did you ever have to make friends in a new place? What did you do?

6. HANDLING SCHOOLWORK THAT IS TOO HARD

Sometimes the work your teacher gives you is just too hard for you. You might feel worried about falling behind.

Expected Behavior:

When you feel that your schoolwork is too hard, you should ask for help.

Meet Charles:

Charles is having trouble with the work in his new math class.

Charles

Meet Ms. Larson:

Ms. Larson is Charles's teacher.

Ms. Larson

THE WRONG WAY

Charles is having trouble with his schoolwork. He is getting upset, but does not ask Ms. Larson for help.

THE RIGHT WAY

Charles is having trouble with his schoolwork. He raises his hand to ask Ms. Larson for help. Ms. Larson is glad to help him.

Look at Charles in *The Wrong Way* comic. Can you see that he is looking down? He is not asking Ms. Larson to help him.

Look at Charles in *The Right Way* comic. Can you see that he looks relieved? He is glad he decided to ask Ms. Larson for help.

Look at Ms. Larson in *The Wrong Way* comic. Can you see that she doesn't know Charles needs help?

Look at Ms. Larson in *The Right Way* comic. Can you see that she is ready to help Charles? She would like him to do well.

What else could Charles have done to let Ms. Larson know he needs help with his schoolwork?

Who else could Charles have gone to for help?

Did you ever need help with schoolwork that was too hard? How did you handle it?

7. DEALING WITH TEST ANXIETY

Do you feel anxious about taking tests? Worrying can give you a headache or a stomachache. It can even keep you from doing your best.

Expected Behavior:

When you are feeling worried about a test you have studied for, remind yourself that you are prepared.

Meet Gabrielle:

Gabrielle is anxious about her history test. She is having trouble concentrating.

Gabrielle

Meet Rich:

Rich is Gabrielle's friend. He is also going to take the history test.

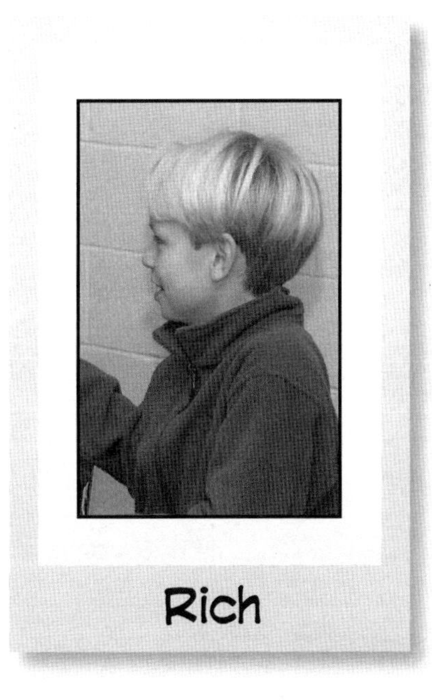
Rich

THE WRONG WAY

Rich sees that Gabrielle is anxious about the test. He reminds Gabrielle that she has studied. She knows the material. But Gabrielle doesn't listen. She keeps worrying.

THE RIGHT WAY

Rich tells Gabrielle that she has studied and is ready. Gabrielle listens. She feels better knowing that she is prepared for the test.

Look at Gabrielle in *The Wrong Way* comic. Can you see that she is not listening to Rich? She is not helping herself feel better.

Look at Gabrielle in *The Right Way* comic. Can you see that she is listening? She is letting Rich help her feel better.

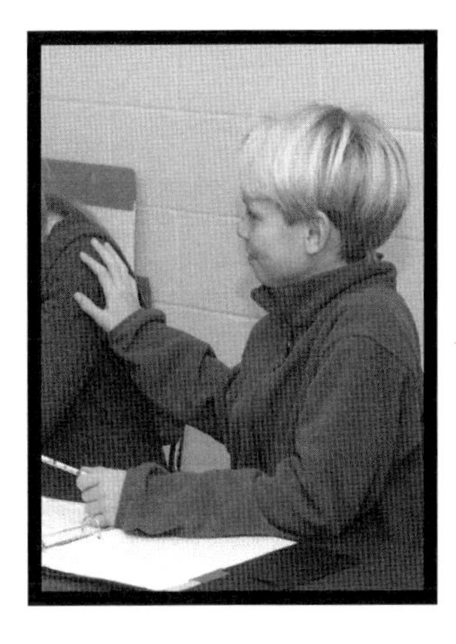

Look at Rich in *The Wrong Way* comic. Can you see that he looks concerned? He wants to help Gabrielle.

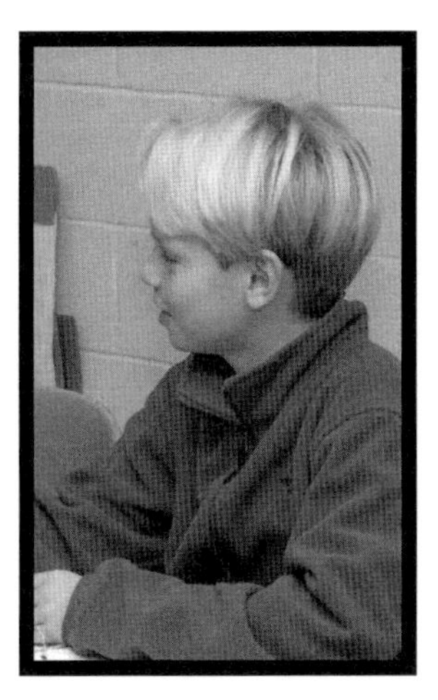

Look at Rich in *The Right Way* comic. Can you see that he is smiling? He is happy to be helping his friend.

What else could Rich have done to help Gabrielle?

Why did Gabrielle keep thinking she would do badly on the test?

Can you think of a time when you were very anxious about taking a test? What did you do?

8. COPING WITH NOISE AND DISTRACTIONS

Have you ever been distracted in school? There are many sights and sounds. They can make it hard to concentrate.

Expected Behavior:

If you get distracted in class, it helps to sit in the front of the classroom.

Meet David:

David gets distracted easily when he is in class.

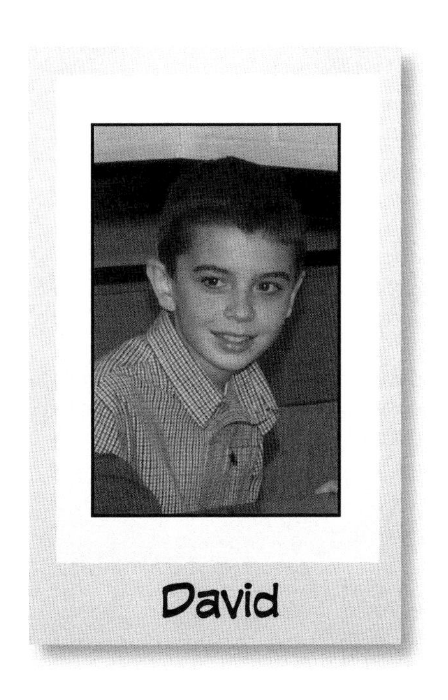

David

Meet Ms. Russo:

Ms. Russo knows that David is having trouble concentrating. She would like to help him.

Ms. Russo

THE WRONG WAY

David sits in the back of the classroom. Ms. Russo suggests that he move to a seat in the front, but David says no.

THE RIGHT WAY

David moves to a seat in the front of the room. Now he can concentrate more easily.

Look at David in *The Wrong Way* comic. Can you see that he is having trouble concentrating?

Look at David in *The Right Way* comic. Can you see that he is smiling? He will find it easier to concentrate.

Look at Ms. Russo in *The Wrong Way* comic. Can you see that she looks concerned? She knows David is distracted and would like him to move to a different seat.

Look at Ms. Russo in *The Right Way* comic. Can you see that she is smiling? She is happy she can help David.

What else could David do to stay focused in the classroom?

How else could Ms. Russo have helped David?

Were you ever distracted in a class? What caused it? How did you handle it?

9. TRYING OUT FOR A SPORT

Playing a sport can be a lot of fun, but trying out for a team can be scary.

Expected Behavior:

You should remember that everyone gets nervous when they are trying out for something.

Meet Charles:

Charles wants to try out for the basketball team. He is afraid he won't make it.

Meet Billy:

Billy is Charles's friend. He is also trying out for the team.

THE WRONG WAY

Charles is very nervous. He knows he is a good basketball player, but he is scared to try out for the team. He tells Billy he is going to leave.

THE RIGHT WAY

Charles knows that everyone trying out is nervous. He tells Billy he will try his best. Billy is happy that Charles will try.

Look at Charles in *The Wrong Way* comic. Can you see that he wants to leave? He is imagining that he will not do well. He is letting his anxiety keep him from trying.

Look at Charles in *The Right Way* comic. Can you see that he looks determined? He is going to try even though he is nervous.

Look at Billy in *The Wrong Way* comic. Can you see that he does not want his friend to leave?

Look at Billy in *The Right Way* comic. Can you see that he is smiling? He is happy that Charles will try his hardest.

What else could Charles have told himself to help him stay at the tryout?

____

____

____

____

____

What else is difficult to try out for and can make you anxious?

____

____

____

____

____

Were you ever anxious about trying out for a sport? Why were you anxious? What did you do to get over it?

____

____

____

____

____

10. PERFORMING ONSTAGE

Performing on a stage can make anyone nervous. It even happens to actors and singers.

Expected Behavior:

When you feel anxious before a performance, you should take a deep breath and remind yourself that it will be okay.

Meet Gabrielle:

Gabrielle has been looking forward to singing in the school talent show, but is feeling anxious now that the day is here.

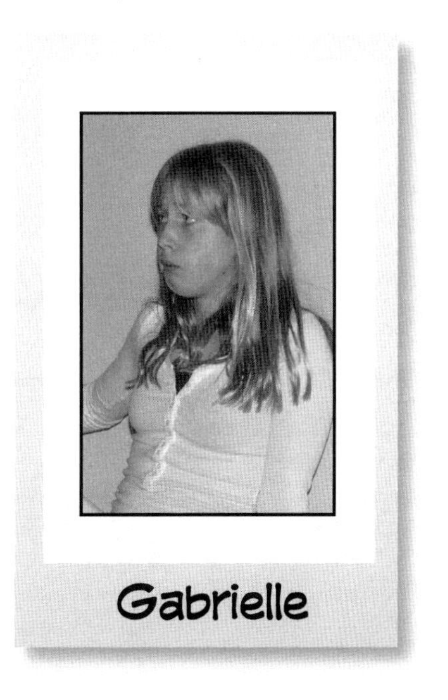

Gabrielle

Meet Rich:

Rich is Gabrielle's friend. He is performing before her in the talent show.

Rich

THE WRONG WAY

Gabrielle is anxious. She thinks everyone will laugh at her. She hears Rich make a mistake during his performance. It makes her even more nervous.

THE RIGHT WAY

Gabrielle asks Rich how he feels. He says he had fun even though he made a mistake. She takes a deep breath and decides to have fun too.

Look at Gabrielle in *The Wrong Way* comic. Can you see that she is nervous? She is worried she will make a mistake. She is not remembering to have fun.

Look at Gabrielle in *The Right Way* comic. Can you see that she is smiling? She is reminding herself that she can have fun no matter what happens.

What else could Gabrielle have told herself so she wouldn't be anxious about the show?

What are some other things people do that might make them anxious?

Did you ever become anxious about having to perform in front of an audience? What did you do?

11. HANDLING SCHOOLWORK THAT UPSETS YOU

Schoolwork can be hard sometimes, and sometimes it may involve touching or seeing things that upset you. It is important that you know how to deal with this.

Expected Behavior:

When you have schoolwork that upsets you, you should ask your teacher what else you could do.

Meet Juan:

Juan's class is doing a project with felt markers. Juan doesn't like the smell of the markers. He avoids them.

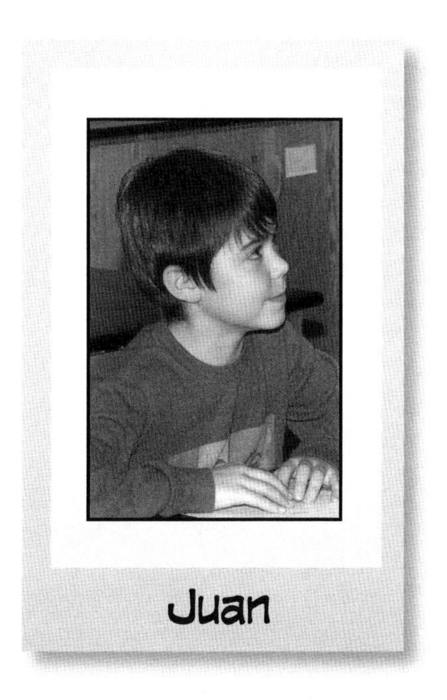

Juan

Meet Ms. Russo:

Ms. Russo is handing out felt markers to the kids in the class.

Ms. Russo

THE WRONG WAY

When Ms. Russo tries to hand markers to Juan, he won't take them. He pushes them away. Ms. Russo is surprised.

THE RIGHT WAY

When Ms. Russo comes to him, Juan tells her he doesn't like the smell of felt markers. Ms. Russo tells Juan he can use colored pencils instead. Ms. Russo is pleased that Juan let her know.

Look at Juan in *The Wrong Way* comic. Can you see that he is looking away from Ms. Russo? He is not telling her he doesn't like using felt markers.

Look at Juan in *The Right Way* comic. Can you see that he is talking to Ms. Russo? He is asking her to let him color some other way.

Look at Ms. Russo in *The Wrong Way* comic. Can you see that she looks concerned? She does not understand what the problem is.

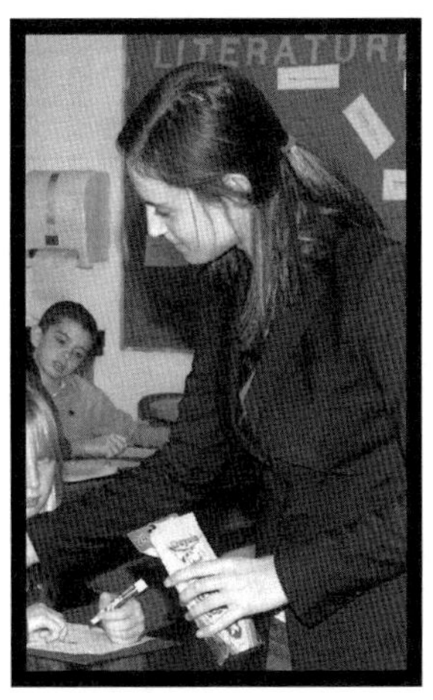

Look at Ms. Russo in *The Right Way* comic. Can you see that she is smiling at Juan? She is glad that Juan told her he does not like using felt markers.

How else could Juan have let Ms. Russo know he didn't like using felt markers because of their smell?

____

____

____

____

____

Have you ever had to do something for school that upset you? What was it?

____

____

____

____

____

What could you say to your teacher if you have to do something that upsets you?

____

____

____

____

____

12. ASKING SOMEONE TO COME OVER

It can be fun when friends come over to share your favorite toys and games, but inviting them may make you nervous.

Expected Behavior:

When you invite friends to come over, you should expect them to be happy you asked.

Meet Juan:

Juan wants to invite Antonia to come over after school.

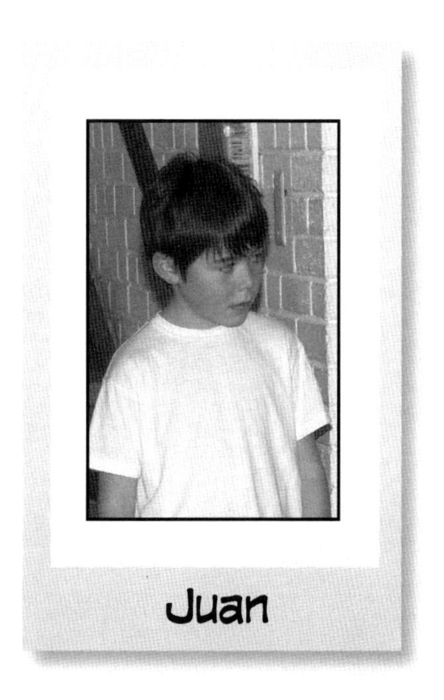

Juan

Meet Antonia:

Antonia is Juan's friend.

Antonia

THE WRONG WAY

Juan wants to invite Antonia over to play with his new game. He thinks they will have fun together. But Juan is too shy. He is afraid Antonia will say no, so he doesn't ask her.

THE RIGHT WAY

Even though he is nervous, Juan invites Antonia to come over. He tells her about the game. Antonia is happy. She says they will have a great time. She is looking forward to the afternoon.

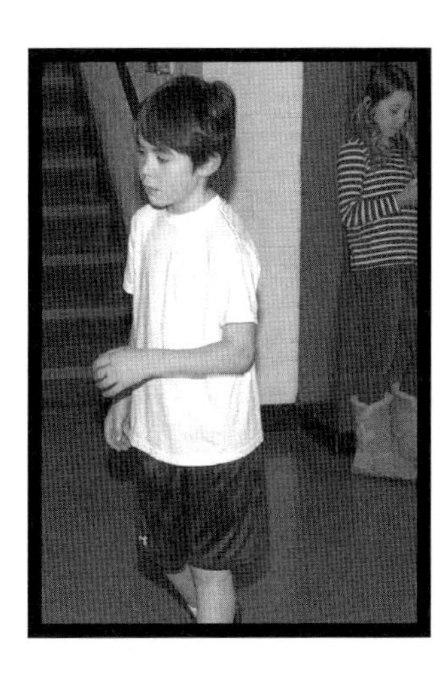

Look at Juan in *The Wrong Way* comic. Can you see that he is heading away from Antonia? He doesn't think Antonia will want to come over.

Look at Juan in *The Right Way* comic. Can you see that he is talking to Antonia? He tells himself that Antonia will be happy to come over.

Look at Antonia in *The Wrong Way* comic. Can you see that she is looking away? She does not know that Juan wants to invite her to play.

Look at Antonia in *The Right Way* comic. Can you see that she is happy? She is looking forward to a fun afternoon.

What else could Juan have said to show Antonia that he wanted her to come over?

Why is it important to ask friends over even if you are nervous or shy?

Has someone ever invited you to come over? How did that person ask you?

13. TALKING TO YOUR TEACHER

Talking to teachers can seem difficult sometimes. They might seem too busy. You might think they won't have patience for what you need. But teachers are happy to help if you are respectful.

Expected Behavior:

When you talk to your teacher, you should find the right time and place.

Meet Benjamin:

Benjamin wants to talk to Ms. Larson about an assignment.

Meet Ms. Larson:

Ms. Larson is Benjamin's teacher.

THE WRONG WAY

Benjamin calls Ms. Larson when she is talking to another student. He doesn't notice that she is busy. Ms. Larson thinks that Benjamin is being rude.

THE RIGHT WAY

Benjamin waits until Ms. Larson is free. Then he asks his question. She is glad he asked her the correct way.

Look at Benjamin in *The Wrong Way* comic. Can you see that he is interrupting Ms. Larson? He is not showing her any consideration.

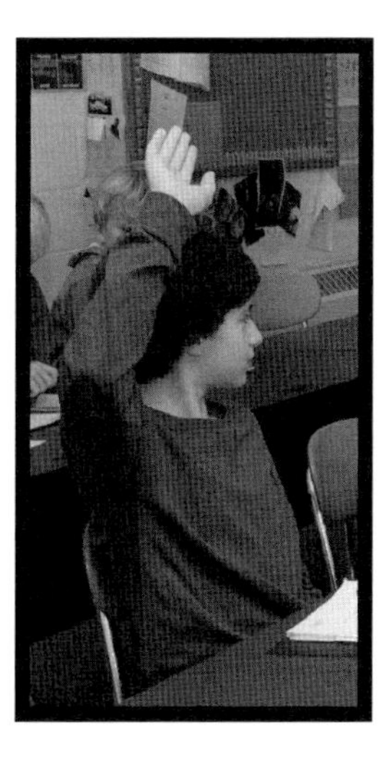

Look at Benjamin in *The Right Way* comic. Can you see that he is waiting for Ms. Larson? He doesn't want to interrupt her.

Look at Ms. Larson in *The Wrong Way* comic. Can you see that she looks displeased? She does not like the way Benjamin interrupted her.

Look at Ms. Larson in *The Right Way* comic. Can you see that she is smiling? She is glad Benjamin waited to talk to her.

How else could Benjamin have approached Ms. Larson?

Why do you think it is important to choose the right place and time to talk to someone?

What do you do when you have to talk your teacher?

14. ACTING CONFIDENT IN FRONT OF THE CLASS

It can be scary to speak in front of the class. When everyone is looking at you, you might think you will do everything wrong. Expecting things to go right can help you feel more confident.

Expected Behavior:

When you have to talk in front of your class, it is important to act confident, even if you don't feel it.

Meet Rich:

Rich has to read a report in front of his class.

Rich

Meet Ms. Larson:

Ms. Larson is listening to his report.

Ms. Larson

THE WRONG WAY

Rich is very nervous. He looks down as he reads. He speaks very quietly. Ms. Larson cannot hear him. She is not happy with his report.

THE RIGHT WAY

Even though Rich is nervous, he stands up straight and speaks in a loud, clear voice. Ms. Larson is very happy with his report.

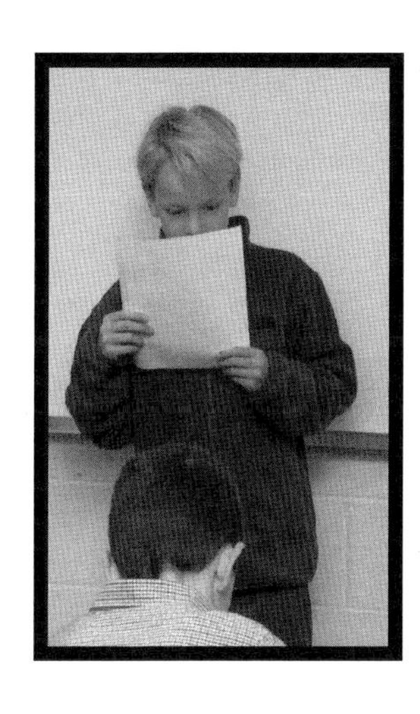

Look at Rich in *The Wrong Way* comic. Can you see that he is looking down? He is not speaking clearly because he is anxious.

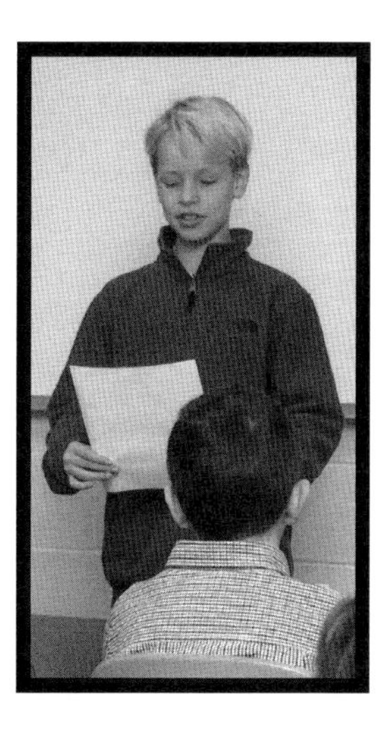

Look at Rich in *The Right Way* comic. Can you see that he is holding his paper away from his face? He is looking up and speaking as clearly as he can.

Look at Ms. Larson in *The Wrong Way* comic. Can you see that she is concentrating hard? She is unhappy with Rich's presentation.

Look at Ms. Larson in *The Right Way* comic. Can you see that she is smiling? She is happy with the way Rich is presenting his report.

What else could Rich have done to seem confident even if he was nervous?

When else should you act brave even if you don't feel brave?

Do you have trouble getting up in front of your class? How do you handle it?

15. FINDING A PLACE TO SIT IN THE CAFETERIA

Most kids love lunchtime. It's a time to get away from schoolwork and be with friends. But what if you don't have anyone to sit with?

Expected Behavior:

When you need a place to sit in the cafeteria, look for a table with just a few kids. They might be looking for friends too.

Meet Charles:

Charles is new at school. He isn't sure where to sit.

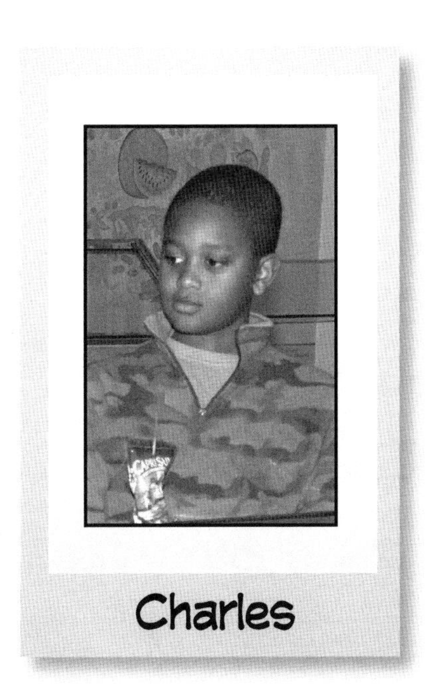

THE WRONG WAY

Charles isn't sure where to sit. He doesn't know anybody. He looks around, then gets frustrated and leaves.

THE RIGHT WAY

Charles finds a table that has a few seats open. He smiles and asks if he can sit down. The kids at the table are happy he has joined them. They enjoy having lunch together.

Look at Charles in *The Wrong Way* comic. Can you see that he is anxious? He is not sure where he should sit.

Look at Charles in *The Right Way* comic. Can you see that he is smiling? He has chosen a table with empty seats so he could make some new friends.

What else could Charles have said to the kids to show that he wanted to join their table?

____

____

____

____

____

Do you have friends you eat lunch with? Do you ever sit at a different table?

____

____

____

____

____

How do you feel when your friends want to eat lunch with someone else? What do you do?

____

____

____

____

____

16. GOING TO A SCHOOL PARTY

School parties can be fun, but some people get nervous. They worry about what they are wearing and what others might think of them. It is important to remember to have a good time.

Expected Behavior:

When you go to a party, you should concentrate on enjoying yourself.

Meet Juan:

Juan is at a school party. He has stepped outside the room for some quiet.

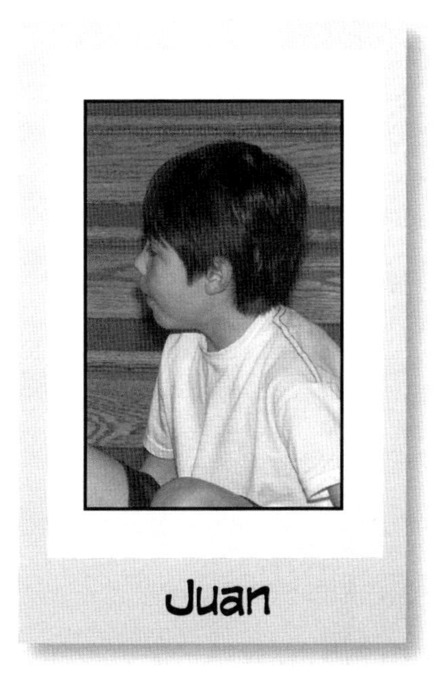

Meet Gabrielle and Antonia:

Gabrielle and Antonia are also taking a break from the party. They are talking to Juan.

THE WRONG WAY

Gabrielle and Antonia are talking about the party. Antonia asks if Juan is having a good time. Juan does not know what to say. He walks away. Gabrielle and Antonia think Juan is being rude.

THE RIGHT WAY

Juan says that he feels a little shy. Gabrielle and Antonia urge him to have fun and offer to help him.

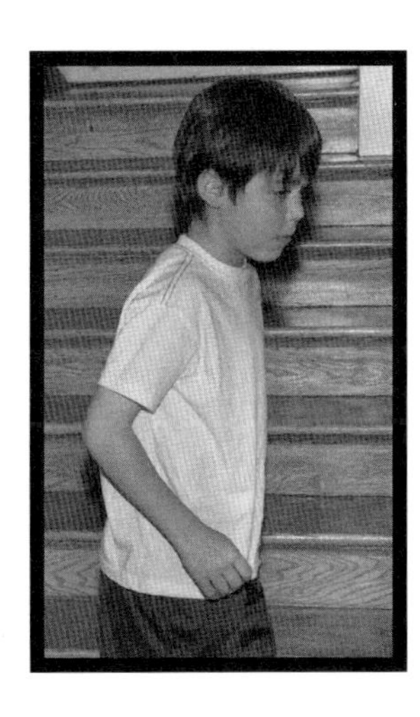

Look at Juan in *The Wrong Way* comic. Can you see that he is walking away? He is worried about having fun.

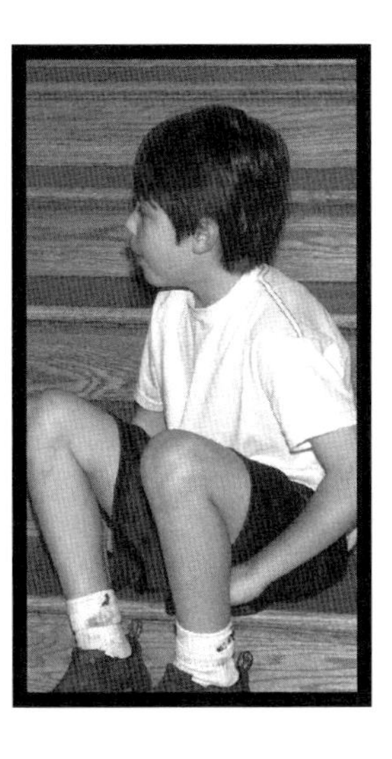

Look at Juan in *The Right Way* comic. Can you see that he is talking? He is telling Gabrielle and Antonia about his concerns.

Look at Gabrielle and Antonia in *The Wrong Way* comic. Can you see that they look confused? They are bothered that Juan walked away.

Look at Gabrielle and Antonia in *The Right Way* comic. Can you see that they are listening to Juan? They are happy to help him have more fun.

What else could Juan have said about the party?

____

____

____

____

____

Why else do you think people feel anxious at school parties?

____

____

____

____

____

Did you ever feel uncomfortable going to a school party? What did you do to help yourself relax?

____

____

____

____

____

17. SPEAKING UP IN A GROUP

Friends like to do things together. But what if your friends want to do something you don't want to do?

Expected Behavior:

When you don't want to do what your friends want to do, you should tell them how you feel.

Meet Benjamin:

Benjamin and his friends are deciding what movie to see this weekend.

Benjamin

Meet Gabrielle and David:

Gabrielle and David are Benjamin's friends.

Gabrielle David

THE WRONG WAY

Gabrielle and David want to see a movie. Benjamin has already seen the movie they are choosing. He doesn't want to spoil the plan, so he doesn't speak up.

THE RIGHT WAY

Benjamin tells Gabrielle and David he has already seen that movie. They are happy to choose another movie instead. Benjamin is pleased that they will change their plan for him.

Look at Benjamin in *The Wrong Way* comic. Can you see that he is unhappy? He doesn't tell his friends why.

Look at Benjamin in *The Right Way* comic. Can you see that he is speaking up? He is happy that the group will see a different movie.

Look at Gabrielle and David in *The Wrong Way* comic. Can you see that are not paying attention to Benjamin? They do not know what he is thinking.

Look at Gabrielle and David in *The Right Way* comic. Can you see that they are talking to Benjamin? They are happy to know what he wants to see.

How else could Benjamin have made his feeling known to Gabrielle and David?

Why is it important for everyone in a group to speak up?

Have you ever had to speak up in a group because you didn't like the plans? What happened?

18. PLAYING WITH OTHERS AT RECESS

Recess gives kids a chance to talk to friends, run around, and have fun. But if you don't have a group of friends to join, you may find it hard to enjoy yourself.

Expected Behavior:

If you want to join a group at recess, you should ask politely.

Meet David:

David is at recess and doesn't have a group to join.

David

Meet Rich, Charles, and Billy:

Rich, Charles, and Billy are playing together.

Rich Charles Billy

THE WRONG WAY

David tries to join Rich, Charles, and Billy by jumping right into their game. They think that David is being rude for interrupting them.

THE RIGHT WAY

David approaches Rich, Charles, and Billy slowly. He says hello. He asks if he can join their game. Rich, Charles, and Billy are glad that David asked politely.

Look at David in *The Wrong Way* comic. Can you see that he is startling Rich, Charles, and Billy? He is disrupting their game.

Look at David in *The Right Way* comic. Can you see that he is asking nicely? He is being friendly to the kids he wants to play with.

Look at Rich, Charles, and Billy in *The Wrong Way* comic. Can you see that they look annoyed? They don't like that David has interrupted their game.

Look at Rich, Charles, and Billy in *The Right Way* comic. Can you see that they responding to David? They are happy that he asked to join their game.

What else could David have done if he wanted to join their game?

____

____

____

____

____

Why is it important to ask correctly when you want to play with others?

____

____

____

____

____

Have you ever asked to join a group in a game? What did you say?

____

____

____

____

____

19. STARTING A CONVERSATION

You have something you want to talk about, but you and your friends are busy. What do you do?

Expected Behavior:

When you have something you want to talk about, you should do it at a time that is good for everyone.

Meet Gabrielle:

Gabrielle is watching a basketball game with her friends. She just remembered something she wants to talk about.

Gabrielle

Meet Antonia and Kate:

Antonia and Kate are watching the game with Gabrielle.

Antonia Kate

THE WRONG WAY

Gabrielle gets up and stands in front of Antonia and Kate. She starts to tell them about a funny thing that happened. They ask Gabrielle to move. They are bothered that she has blocked the game.

THE RIGHT WAY

Gabrielle waits until the game is over. She asks Antonia and Kate if they want to hear something funny. They both enjoy Gabrielle's story.

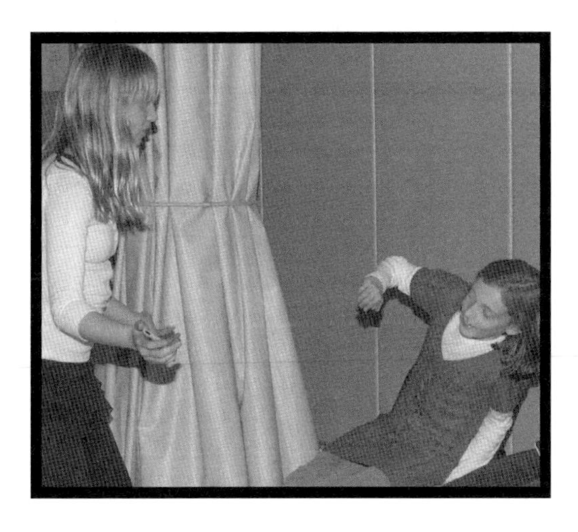

Look at Gabrielle in *The Wrong Way* comic. Can you see that she is standing in front of her friends? She is blocking their view of the game.

Look at Gabrielle in *The Right Way* comic. Can you see that she is talking at a time when her friends can listen? She has been considerate.

Look at Antonia and Kate in *The Wrong Way* comic. Can you see that they are trying to see around Gabrielle? They are upset because she has blocked their view.

Look at Antonia and Kate in *The Right Way* comic. Can you see that they are smiling? They are happy to listen to what Gabrielle wants to say.

What else could Gabrielle have said if she wanted to start a conversation with her friends?

____

____

____

____

____

Has someone ever tried to start a conversation with you when you were busy doing something else? How did you feel?

____

____

____

____

____

Can you think of another time when it would not be good to start a conversation with someone?

____

____

____

____

____

20. RECEIVING COMPLIMENTS

It's nice to get a compliment, but it can be embarrassing too. How should you respond? What should you say?

Expected Behavior:

When you receive a compliment, you should respond politely even if you feel shy.

Meet Antonia:

Antonia is being complimented by her friend Kate.

Antonia

Meet Kate:

Kate is complimenting Antonia.

Kate

THE WRONG WAY

Antonia looks away from Kate. She doesn't answer when Kate compliments her. Kate is puzzled by Antonia's reaction.

THE RIGHT WAY

Antonia smiles at Kate. She says thanks. Kate is happy with Antonia's reaction.

Look at Antonia in *The Wrong Way* comic. Can you see that she is looking away while Kate is talking to her? She is not accepting her compliment.

Look at Antonia in *The Right Way* comic. Can you see that she is smiling? She is showing Kate that she is happy with her compliment.

Look at Kate in *The Wrong Way* comic. Can you see that she looks puzzled? She thought Antonia would like her compliment.

Look at Kate in *The Right Way* comic. Can you see that she is smiling? She is glad that Antonia took her compliment well.

What else could Antonia have done to show that she appreciated Kate's compliment?

____

____

____

____

____

What can you do if someone doesn't want to be complimented?

____

____

____

____

____

Have you ever felt shy or awkward when someone complimented you? Tell what happened.

____

____

____

____

____

21. USING A PUBLIC BATHROOM

Some people feel shy about using public bathrooms. But if you have to go, you will have to use the bathroom at school.

Expected Behavior:

When you need to use a public bathroom, you should feel comfortable enough to do it.

Meet Benjamin:

Benjamin needs to use the bathroom.

Meet David:

David is Benjamin's friend. He also needs to use the bathroom.

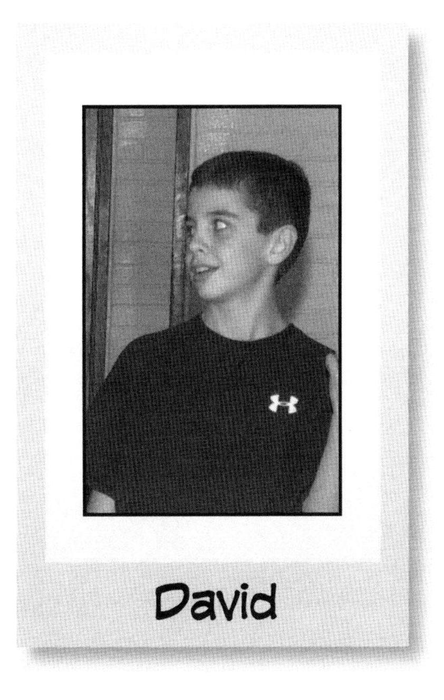

THE WRONG WAY

David walks into the bathroom. Benjamin feels too shy to use a public bathroom. He walks away.

THE RIGHT WAY

Benjamin feels shy about going into the bathroom. David tells him that it will be okay. He goes ahead and uses the bathroom.

Look at Benjamin in *The Wrong Way* comic. Can you see that he is walking away? He won't use the public bathroom even though his friend David will.

Look at Benjamin in *The Right Way* comic. Can you see that he is trusting his friend's advice?

What else could David have said to let Benjamin know what he thought?

Talking to a friend is one good way to learn more about a topic. How else could Benjamin have learned more about using public bathrooms?

Are there places you don't like to go? Where?

22. WAITING FOR A PARENT WHO IS LATE

A grownup who is supposed to pick you up may be late sometimes. When you have to wait, you might feel worried.

Expected Behavior:

When you are waiting to be picked up and your parent is late, you should remain calm.

Meet Gabrielle:

Gabrielle is waiting for her mother to pick her up after school.

Gabrielle

Meet Ms. Clement:

Ms. Clement is Gabrielle's teacher. She sees Gabrielle sitting outside.

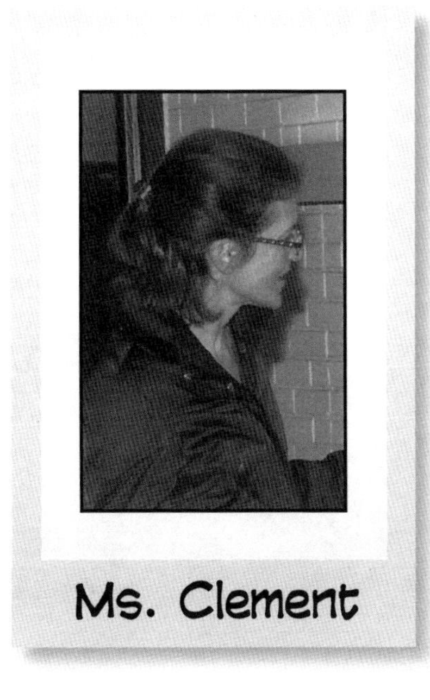

Ms. Clement

THE WRONG WAY

Ms. Clement sees Gabrielle waiting. She asks why Gabrielle is still there. Gabrielle says that no one has come to pick her up.

THE RIGHT WAY

When Ms. Clement asks why Gabrielle is still waiting, Gabrielle explains that her mother always picks her up but is just a bit late today. Ms. Clement is glad to know Gabrielle is okay.

Look at Gabrielle in *The Wrong Way* comic. Can you see that she looks upset? Her reaction makes Ms. Clement worry that she has no ride home.

Look at Gabrielle in *The Right Way* comic. Can you see that she is smiling? She is letting Ms. Clement know that she is all right even though her mother is late.

Look at Ms. Clement in *The Wrong Way* comic. Can you see that she looks worried? She thinks that Gabrielle has no ride home.

Look at Ms. Clement in *The Right Way* comic. Can you see that she looks relaxed talking to Gabrielle? She knows that Gabrielle will be picked up soon.

What else could Gabrielle have said to Ms. Clement to let her know she was okay?

How do you feel when someone is late to pick you up? Do you worry right away?

What can you do to calm yourself when someone is late?

23. ASKING FOR HELP

Do you find it difficult to ask for help? Asking for help can be hard, but sometimes it is necessary, so it is important to know how to ask the right way.

Expected Behavior:

When you need to ask for help, you should pick the right time.

Meet Benjamin:

Benjamin needs help opening his locker.

Meet Rich:

Rich is opening his own locker.

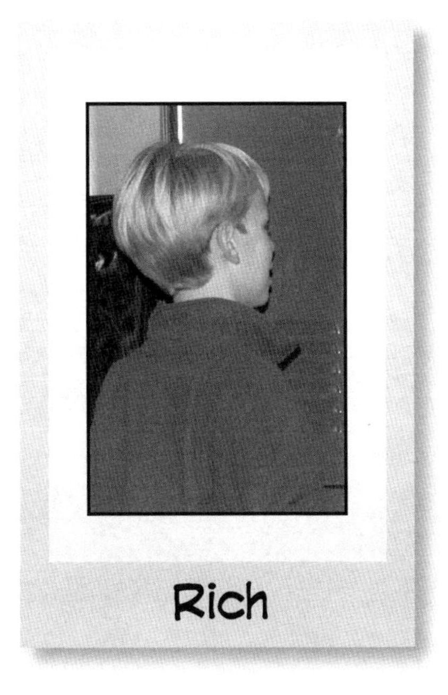

THE WRONG WAY

Benjamin asks for help while Rich is busy. Rich is upset with Benjamin for interrupting him and not waiting.

THE RIGHT WAY

Benjamin waits for Rich to finish opening his own locker before he asks for help. He waits for Rich to answer. Rich is happy to help Benjamin.

Look at Benjamin in *The Wrong Way* comic. Can you see that he is interrupting Rich? He is ignoring the fact that Rich is busy.

Look at Benjamin in *The Right Way* comic. Can you see that he is not talking? He is waiting patiently for Rich to finish.

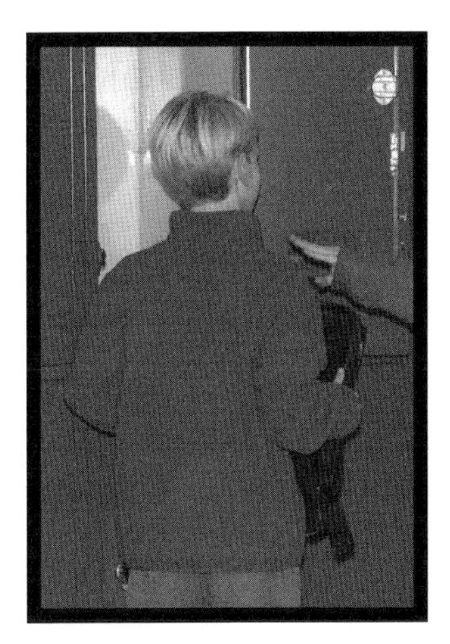

Look at Rich in *The Wrong Way* comic. Can you see that he is trying to ignore Benjamin? He is bothered by the interruption.

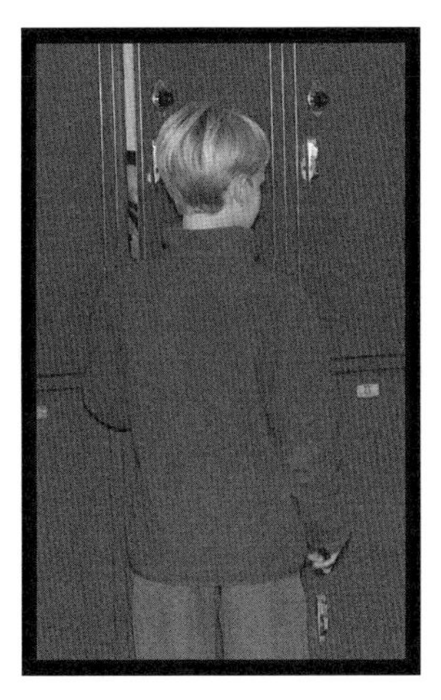

Look at Rich in *The Right Way* comic. Can you see that he is talking to Benjamin? He is happy that Benjamin did not disturb him while he was opening his locker.

What else could Benjamin have said to ask for Rich's help the right way?

How else could Benjamin have gotten his locker open?

Has anyone ever asked you for help at a bad time? How did you let that person know it was a bad time?

24. LEAVING CLASS EARLY

Sometimes you may have to leave class early. How do you leave quietly? How do you keep from disturbing others? It can be tricky, but there's a right way to do it.

Expected Behavior:

When you have to leave a class early, you should try to do it without disrupting others.

Meet Kate:

Kate has her teacher's permission to leave class early.

Meet Ms. Larson:

Ms. Larson is Kate's teacher.

THE WRONG WAY

When it is time for her to leave, Kate stops to say goodbye to her friend. Ms. Larson wants to continue teaching the lesson. She asks Kate to be more quiet.

THE RIGHT WAY

Kate gathers her books as quietly as she can. She quickly says goodbye to Ms. Larson. Ms. Larson is pleased that she did not disrupt the class.

Look at Kate in *The Wrong Way* comic. Can you see that she is talking to her friend? She ignores the fact that Ms. Larson is teaching.

Look at Kate in *The Right Way* comic. Can you see that she is talking only to Ms. Larson? She is leaving as quickly and quietly as she can.

Look at Ms. Larson in *The Wrong Way* comic. Can you see that she is talking to Kate? She would like Kate to leave without talking to other students.

Look at Ms. Larson in *The Right Way* comic. Can you see that she is happy? She is glad that Kate is leaving the class so quietly.

What else could Kate have done to leave the class without disturbing the other students?

____

____

____

____

____

Do you think Ms. Larson was right to be bothered when Kate made noise leaving the class? Why?

____

____

____

____

____

Have you ever had to leave a class before it was over? How did you manage to keep quiet?

____

____

____

____

____

25. WALKING DOWN A HALLWAY ALONE

It can feel awkward to walk down the hallway alone. You might think people are talking about you, or about your clothes or the way you look.

Expected Behavior:

When you are walking down a hallway alone, you should not think that everyone is judging you.

Meet Antonia:

Antonia is walking to her next class alone.

Antonia

Meet Kate:

Kate is a student Antonia does not know. She is standing with two of her friends.

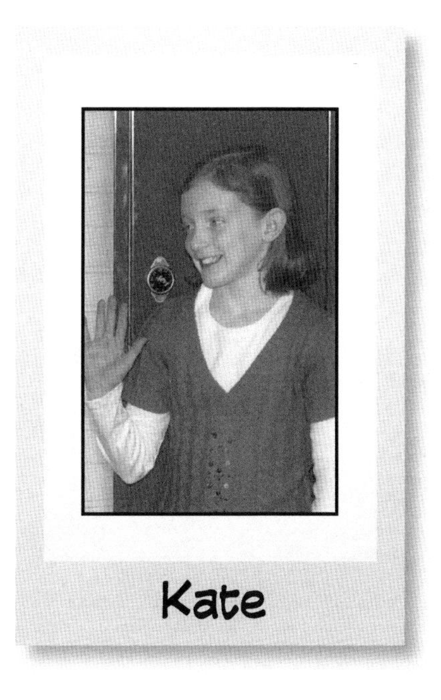

Kate

THE WRONG WAY

Antonia keeps her head down when she walks in the hallway. She looks shy. When Kate notices her, Antonia looks away because she thinks Kate might be judging her.

THE RIGHT WAY

Antonia sees Kate looking at her, so she smiles and says hello. Kate smiles back. Antonia is happy that she didn't think Kate was judging her.

Look at Antonia in *The Wrong Way* comic. Can you see that she is turning away from Kate? She is worried that Kate might be judging her.

Look at Antonia in *The Right Way* comic. Can you see that she is smiling? She is making a new friend instead of worrying about being judged.

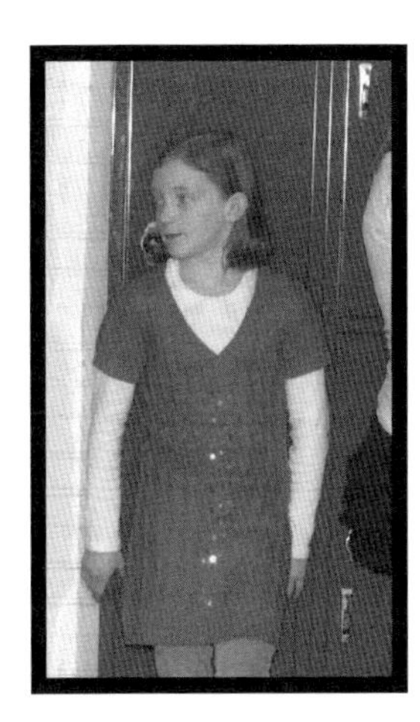

Look at Kate in *The Wrong Way* comic. Can you see that she is looking right at Antonia? She notices that Antonia looks shy.

Look at Kate in *The Right Way* comic. Can you see that she is smiling? She is happy that Antonia was friendly to her.

What else could Antonia have said to Kate to get to know her?

___

___

___

___

___

What might happen if Antonia tries smiling again the next time she thinks she is being judged?

___

___

___

___

___

Do you feel like people are judging you when you are walking alone? What do you imagine they are thinking?

___

___

___

___

___